Purchased

Purchased

British Library Cataloguing in Publication Data

Deshpande, Chris
    Five stones and knuckle bones.—(Friends series)
    1. Sports—Juvenile literature 2 Games—
    Juvenile literature
    I. Title   II. Matthews, Jenny III. series
    796   GU704

    ISBN 0-7136-2987-8

Published by A & C Black (Publishers) Ltd
35 Bedford Row, London WC1R 4JH

Acknowledgements
The author and publisher would like to thank the staff, parents and
children of Cherry Orchard Primary School, especially Claire Davies,
June Markham and Olga Owen.

Filmset by August Filmsetting, Haydock, St Helens
Printed in Belgium by Henri Proost & Cie Pvba

Five stones and knuckle bones

Chris Deshpande
Photographs by Jenny Matthews

A & C Black · London

Leela is starting her new school today.

'I wonder what it will be like, Mum.
Will it be like my old school in London, Dad?'

When Mum and Dad have gone, Leela feels a bit scared.

'Come on Leela. I'll take you to your classroom,' says Mrs Owen, the headteacher. 'You're in Class 4 and your teacher is Miss Davies.'

Miss Davies chats to Leela about her old school and tries to make her feel happier.

Gale and Oliver try to make friends, too. But Leela is feeling very shy and doesn't know what to say.

Playtime!
Everyone is in a hurry
to put on their coats.

5

'Come on, let's play.'

Leela is left in the empty cloakroom.
I don't like it here, she thinks. I wish
I was back at my old school. I had lots of
friends there.

I wonder where Gale and Oliver are.
They might play with me.

Leela wanders into the playground and sees some children playing marbles.

That looks fun, she thinks. I'll go and watch. Maybe they'll ask me to play.

Inderjit wins the game. She knocks the most marbles out of the circle.

I know that game. It's Bombadiers, thinks
Leela. I played it with my cousins in Delhi.

I'd like to play Brown Girl in the Ring, but if I ask them, they might say no. I wish I could find Gale and Oliver.

They're not playing
Hopscotch...

. . . or on the slide.

And I'll never find
them in that lot,
thinks Leela.
I wonder what
that game is.

Gale and Oliver aren't playing with the skipping rope either, but Leela stays to watch for a while.

She used to play 'Higher and higher' and 'Lower and lower' with Rupal and Joanna at her old school.

4

Is that Gale playing Jacks? I hope not because
I can't play that, it's too hard.

15

People-puzzle is good
fun to play, but the game
has already started.

I bet it will take ages
to untangle them,
thinks Leela.

Freeze! It's Grandmother's footsteps, and he
mustn't see you move. Who is going to get
there first?

Gale and Oliver aren't here either. I wish
playtime was over, thinks Leela. I want
my mum and dad. I want to go home.

I suppose I'll just have to play on my own. Hey, these footsteps are big. They must be giant's footsteps.

'Hi, Leela! There you are.' It is Gale and Oliver.
'What are you doing?' asks Oliver.
'Nothing,' says Leela.

'Let's play Follow my leader, and you can
be leader,' says Gale.

'This is great,' laughs Leela.

The line gets longer and longer as more
children join in.

Soon, Miss Davies rings the bell and playtime is over.

I'm going to like this school, thinks Leela, as she and her new friends all go inside together.

More about playground games

Do you know all the games in this book? This is how some of them are played. You may know them with different rules.

Marbles

This is a very old game. It was played in Ancient Egypt. There are lots of ways to play marbles. Here are two:
In Bombadiers, a circle is drawn on the ground and each person puts 2 or 3 marbles in a pile in the middle of the circle. They then take turns to drop one marble on to the pile. If someone knocks a marble out of the circle, they can keep it. They keep playing until all the marbles have been won.

Another way of playing marbles is to flick or roll your marble along the ground to try and knock the other marbles out of the circle.

Brown Girl in the Ring

This is a well known game played in the Caribbean. It is a very old game, and is mentioned in one of the Anancy stories from Africa.

To play, you make a circle with one person in the middle. The people in the circle dance round, singing the song:

'There's a brown girl in the ring
Tra la la la la
There's a brown girl in the ring
Tra la la la la
There's a brown girl in the ring
Tra la la la la
For she likes sugar and I like plum'*

The person in the middle of the circle has to do something, like hopping or clapping hands and the others have to copy it. The person in the middle chooses the next person to go in the middle of the ring.

Do you know any other 'ring' games, like 'Farmer in his dell'?

*(This is the first verse of the song, you can read the rest in a book of songs called 'Mango Spice', published by A & C Black.)

Hopscotch

No one knows where this game began, but it's played in Britain, Russia, India, China and many other countries.

To play, you first need to draw out the hopscotch squares ('scotch' is an old English word, meaning 'to mark or draw lightly').

You hop on the single squares, like 1 and 4. You jump on the double squares with one foot on each square.

Start by tossing a stone on to the square marked 1. You have to jump over the square with the stone on it. When you reach the end, turn and then hop and jump until you reach the stone. Pick up the stone and carry on until you jump off the squares. You can then toss the stone to the next number. Carry on this way until you have thrown the stone on to every square. If you miss a square, your turn finishes.

The other games which Leela and her friends played were: skipping games, Jacks, People-puzzle, Grandmother's footsteps and Follow my leader. If you don't know these games, try and find out how to play them.

Things to do

1. Make a list of all the playground games which you and your friends like to play. Draw a bar chart, showing how many people like each game best. It might look a bit like this:

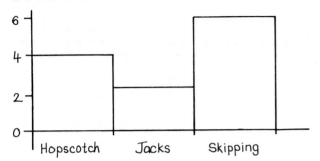

2. Try to find out where your favourite games started and the different ways they are played. Two good books to use are '*Games of the World*', published by UNICEF and '*Let's play Asian Children's Games*' published by the Asian Cultural Centre for UNESCO. You may enjoy playing your favourite games with different rules.

3. Sometimes children miss out on games. This might be because your friends think of some as 'girls' games' and some as 'boys' games'. Try listing your games like this:

Girls' Games	Boys' Games	Both
Skipping	Football	Marbles

When you have made your list, why not play one of the games in a way that you wouldn't normally play it?

4. Some games are played with lots of people, some with just a few and some with just one person. How many players do you need for your favourite games? Before you start, does it take a long time to work out how you're going to play? Which games take longest to play?

Try making a list of games, showing how many players they have, how long they take to prepare and how long it takes to play each game.

5. Five stones and Knuckle bones are two different names for Jacks. See if you can find out where the names come from. Do you know any other names for Jacks?

6. How many skipping rhymes do you know? Try and make up some of your own. Do you know any dipping rhymes to start a game or to decide who will be 'it'? You could make a tape of all the rhymes you know and the ones you have made up.

7. Do you play the same games as your parents or grandparents? Why not learn some of the games and rhymes which they know?

8. Try to find out which games children in other countries like to play. You could look at games played in Asia, Africa, the Caribbean, America and Europe. You might be surprised by how many you know.

9. You could find out about indoor games such as board games. Did you know that Snakes and ladders and Ludo both started in India?

PRINTED IN BELGIUM BY

INTERNATIONAL BOOK PRODUCTION